Number, Ratio & Alge

Page 10 — Decimals, Fractions and Percentages

1) $\frac{2}{3} > 50\%$ $\frac{33}{50} = 0.66$

   $\frac{8}{10} > \frac{18}{25}$ $0.48 > \frac{90}{200}$

2) Andrei, E.g. $\frac{7}{20} = \frac{35}{100} = 35\%$, which is more than 28%.

3) A, C, B

4)
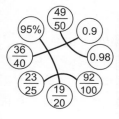

Pages 11 to 13 — Proportion and Ratio

1) 450 g carrots
   300 g courgettes

2) 10.8 kg
   4 cakes

3) 7.5 m

4) 84 acres
   (One seventh = 60 ÷ 5 = 12 acres,
   so seven sevenths = 12 × 7)

5) 80 white tiles

6) 5 : 2
   Yes, E.g. The width has been doubled, from 24 cm
   to 48 cm, so the length and total perimeter will
   be doubled / increase by a scale factor of 2.

7) 9 mm

8) Peter gets £27, Jemima gets £63
   (3 + 7 = 10 parts, £90 ÷ 10 = £9 per part,
   3 × £9 = £27 and 7 × £9 = £63)

9) 26th August

10) Yes, E.g. There are 30 – 12 – 9 = 9 pink buttons
    and 9 blue buttons. 9 : 9 simplifies to 1 : 1.
    150 buttons
    12 buttons

11) Apples: 490 g, Cherries: 140 g, Rhubarb: 210 g

Pages 14 to 16 — Mul

1) 76, 72

2) 4, 8, 16

3)

	Factor of 60	Not a factor of 60
Multiple of 3	12, 15	18
Not a multiple of 3	10, 20	11, 13, 14, 16, 17, 19

4) 120 cm
   (Multiples of 24 = 24, 48, 72, 96, 120...
   The first multiple of 15 in the list is 120.)

5) FALSE
   TRUE
   FALSE

6) 1, 5

7) 17

8) No, E.g. There are only 5 prime numbers
   between 31 and 49 (31, 37, 41, 43 and 47).

9) E.g. For 12 to be a factor, the only possible month is 12
   (December), and the only possible days are 12 and 24.
   So Mika's birthday is the 12th or 24th December.

10) 3 × 5 = 15 OR 5 × 3 = 15

11) E.g. 2 × 3 × 5 × 7
    Yes, E.g. 2, 3, 5 and 7 are the four smallest
    prime numbers. To get a smaller number than
    210 would mean repeating one of 2, 3 or 5.

Pages 17 and 18 — Square and Cube Numbers

1) $4^2 + 3^2 = 5^2$, $10^2 - 6^2 = 8^2$

2) E.g. 1 is also a factor of 75 and 1 is a square number.

3) 1 cm
   (Large side length = 9 cm, small side length = 7 cm.
   9 – 7 = 2 cm, X = 2 cm ÷ 2.)

4) 1 × 8 = 8 OR 8 × 1 = 8
   125 – 64 = 61

5) TRUE
   FALSE
   TRUE
   FALSE

6) No, E.g. Using 4 blocks for length, width and
   height uses 4^3 = 64 blocks (too few), and using
   5 blocks uses 5^3 = 125 blocks (too many).
   So there is no way of using exactly 100 blocks.

7) 60 years
   (Jen must be 16 as it's the only square in the teens, so
   Milly is 4 and Karl is 4^3 = 64. Difference is 64 – 4.)

Number, Ratio & Algebra

Section 2 — Calculations

Pages 19 and 20 — Adding and Subtracting

1) 17 898
2) 1 030 512
3) 1 699 988
4) £2 623 410
   (£1 340 500 – £500 000 = £840 500.
   £840 500 + £870 895 + £912 015)
5) 8.544 km
6) £50.43
   (Thursday: £57.98
   Wednesday: £57.98 + £8.50 = £66.48
   Tuesday: £66.48 – £16.05 = £50.43)
7) 87.855 litres
   (21.645 litres + 10.5 litres = 32.145 litres.
   120 litres – 32.145 litres)

Page 21 — Adding and Subtracting Fractions

1) $\frac{11}{20}$
2) $5\frac{1}{2} + \frac{3}{7} = 5\frac{13}{14}$, $5\frac{1}{2} - \frac{5}{6} = 4\frac{2}{3}$
3) $\frac{17}{45}$
4) $1\frac{13}{20}$ litres

Pages 22 to 25 — Multiplying and Dividing

1) 720 000
   8 lorries, 32 lorries
2) 1079 parcels
3) 19 640 bytes
4) 13 bookcases
   (1060 ÷ 80 = 13 remainder 20)
5) (10 + 64) ÷ 4 × 10
6) $5 \times 15 + 5^2 - 10^2$
7) 1620 treats
8) 298 m²
   (2 × 14 = 28. 8344 m² ÷ 28)
9) 3.456, 3456
   80 360, 8.036
10) nine point zero five seven
11) 1 tenth or 0.1
    2 tens or 20
    3 hundreds or 300
12) £120.75
13) 8008.5
14) 2262.5
15) £207.60
16) 337.62 cm
    (19.86 cm × 17)
17) 112.25 g
    (6286 g ÷ 56)

Page 26 — Multiplying and Dividing Fractions

1) $\frac{1}{6}$
2) $\frac{5}{11} \times \frac{3}{8} = \frac{15}{88}$, $\frac{5}{6} \times 12 = 10$
3) $\frac{2}{15}$
   $(1 - \frac{1}{5} = \frac{4}{5}, \frac{4}{5} \times \frac{1}{6} = \frac{4}{30})$
4) $\frac{8}{15} \div 4 = \frac{2}{15}$, $\frac{2}{3} \div 8 = \frac{1}{12}$

Pages 27 to 29 — Checking and Estimating

1)

Calculation	Inverse
90 033 – 412 = 89 621	89 621 + 412 = 90 033
21 009 + 36 712 = 57 721	E.g. 57 721 – 36 712 = 21 009
E.g. 49 × 332 = 16 268	16 268 ÷ 49 = 332
E.g. 77 696 ÷ 8 = 9712	9712 × 8 = 77 696

2) E.g. 5000 × 30
   E.g. 70 000 + 130 000
   E.g. 9900 ÷ 10

3)

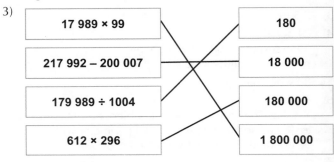

4) 897 × 92, 8103 × 9
5) E.g. £6400 (£8 × 800)
   Less, E.g. £7.99 and 798 are both rounded up,
   so the real amount must be less than this.
6) E.g. 30 000 cm (100 × 300 cm)
   E.g. 500 000 kg (100 × 5 × 1000 kg)
7) 18 minutes
   (143.95 litres rounds to 144 litres.
   7.98 litres rounds to 8 litres. 144 ÷ 8)
8) 240 mm
   1.2 mm
   E.g. 1620 cm²
   (9.02 cm rounds to 9 cm to the nearest cm.
   So, 1 square is approximately 9 × 9 = 81 cm²
   and 20 squares is approximately 81 cm² × 20)

CGP

KS2 Maths
SAT Buster Stretch
Extra practice to challenge pupils aiming for a high score

Answer Book

Arithmetic • Number, Ratio & Algebra
Geometry, Measures & Statistics

Number, Ratio & Algebra

Number, Ratio & Algebra
Section 1 — Number and Ratio

Page 1 — Place Value and Roman Numerals

1)
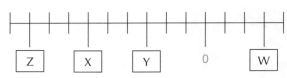
70 000 or 7 ten thousands

2) 9 876 542
Nine million, eight hundred and seventy-six thousand, five hundred and forty-two

3) 1995
220 years old
(1995 + 215 = 2210 = MMCCX, so the year is MMCCXV = 2215, 2215 − 1995)

Pages 2 to 4 — Ordering Numbers and Rounding

1) 989 999, 999 999, 1 009 999

2) C, D, A, B, E
E.g. 1 100 000
(Allow any number between 1 096 953 and 1 221 425.)

3) 1 224 567, 1 334 567
432 567, 1 234 467

4) 37 952 + 10 **<** 38 972 − 10
809 765 + 1000 **=** 811 765 − 1000
1 043 201 − 100 **>** 943 201 + 100
92 989 + 10 000 **>** 100 000 − 100

5) W = 3, X = −6
Y = −3, Z = −9

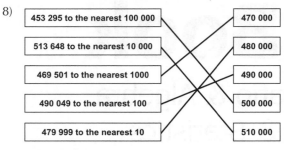

6) 380 metres above sea level
(800 + 40 = 840, 840 ÷ 2 = 420, −40 + 420)

7) 0 °C
Yes, E.g. It will only take 6 × 5 = 30 minutes to cool the pie to 0 °C (the same as the pizza), so after an hour it will be at −12 °C (colder than the pizza).

8)

453 295 to the nearest 100 000	470 000
513 648 to the nearest 10 000	480 000
469 501 to the nearest 1000	490 000
490 049 to the nearest 100	500 000
479 999 to the nearest 10	510 000

9) 384 402 km
384 999 km

10) Yes, E.g. The smallest possible number of cats (9 950 000) is still larger than the largest possible number of dogs (9 499 999).

Pages 5 and 6 — Decimals

1) 27.91

2)
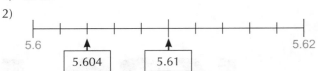

3) 0.149

4) Dobbert
Will and Bunny
2.546 kg, 2.559 kg, 2.56 kg, 2.569 kg

5) 9.5 m
(2.4 + 3.3 + 3.8)

6) 100.054 > 100.05   55 < 55.005
−0.384 < −0.38   −1.76 > −1.765
−20.04 < −20.009   −9.99 < −9.899

7) No, E.g. The rounded calculation would be 4 × 5 + 5, which is 20 + 5 = 25.

Pages 7 and 8 — Fractions

1) $\frac{60}{100}$, $\frac{40}{200}$, $\frac{15}{25}$

2) E.g. Sean: $\frac{39}{75}$, Pia: $\frac{45}{75}$
Pia

3) Yes, E.g. Both fractions can be simplified to $\frac{7}{12}$.

4)

5) $\frac{11}{2}$ inches, $\frac{15}{4}$ inches, $2\frac{15}{16}$ inches, $2\frac{7}{8}$ inches

6) 3
1
2

7) $2\frac{4}{9}$, $3\frac{1}{3}$, $4\frac{2}{9}$, $5\frac{1}{9}$, 6

Page 9 — Percentages

1) 15%

2) 448 hats

3) 105 blue cars
(Red: 300 ÷ 4 = 75, Silver: 4 × (300 ÷ 10) = 120, Blue: 300 − 75 − 120)
15%

4) Huw, E.g. 15% × 10 will give a larger amount than 25% × 5.

Number, Ratio & Algebra

Section 3 — Problem Solving and Algebra

Pages 30 to 32 — Wordy Problems

1) 9 856 421
8 246 951

2) £4.55
£1.68
800 g
(89p ≈ 90p, 720 ÷ 90 = 8 lots of 100 g)

3) 5 cows
200 animals
(1 + 3 + 36 = 40, so for every cow,
there are 40 animals, 40 × 5)

4) $\frac{5}{12}$
40 g
($\frac{1}{12}$ of 960 g = 960 ÷ 12 = 80 g,
$\frac{5}{12}$ of 960 g = 80 × 5 = 400 g,
so 960 – 400 = 560 g left, 1 slice = 560 ÷ 14)

5) 1125 m
720 steps
(1125 ÷ 100 = 11.25, 64 × 11.25)

6) Ben = 3, Ceara = 24, Dan = 12

Pages 33 and 34 — Patterns and Sequences

1) subtract 6 from the previous number
–20

2) 12, 44

3) 10, 18

4) $12\frac{1}{4}$, $8\frac{3}{4}$, $5\frac{1}{4}$, $1\frac{3}{4}$

5) 6.5, 11.2, 15.9, 20.6, 25.3, 30

6) 130

7)

42 buttons
(E.g. Term 20 will have 20 buttons in the top row,
2 buttons in the middle row and 20 buttons in the
bottom row, 20 + 2 + 20)

Pages 35 to 39 — Formulas

1) 33 cm²

2) total number of cups of water = 8 × number of days

3) total amount of money made = 3 × number of slices sold
£72

4) 25 m³
15 cm²
($40 = \frac{\text{base area} \times 8}{3}$, 120 = base area × 8,
base area = 120 ÷ 8)

5) 118 biscuits

6) $C = 15 + 4h$
£39

7) $N = 5s$
$M = 19 + 2s$
$s = 7$
($33 = 19 + 2s$, $2s = 33 – 19 = 14$, $s = 14 ÷ 2$)

8) 3, 9, 15, 21, 27

9) $7n + 23$

10) $x = 32$
(Dot = 100 – 4 = 96, $3x = 96$, $x = 96 ÷ 3$)

11) E.g. $2.25 = 5W + 0.5$
$W = 0.35$
($1.75 = 5W$, $W = 1.75 ÷ 5$)

12) E.g. $2s + 4j = 20$
$s = 8$, $j = 1$ OR
$s = 6$, $j = 2$ OR
$s = 4$, $j = 3$

13) $s = 4n – 1$
$s = 19$
$n = 9$

14) $X = 5T + 3P + 2C$
46 points
(Total scored by Howlers = (5 × 3) + (3 × 4) + (2 × 1)
= 15 + 12 + 2 = 29 points
Total scored by Clangers = 29 + 17)

	Pair 1	Pair 2	Pair 3
T	1	4	7
P	13	8	3

($5T + 3P + 2 = 46$, $5T + 3P = 44$)

Geometry, Measures & Statistics

Geometry, Measures & Statistics

Section 1 — Geometry

Pages 1 and 2 — 2D Shapes

1) regular heptagon
   regular hexagon
   equilateral triangle
   kite
   parallelogram

2) FALSE
   TRUE
   FALSE

3) For each row, the following should be ticked:
   Isosceles, Right-angled
   Equilateral, Isosceles, Right-angled
   Isosceles

4) Similarity: E.g. They are both pentagons / have 5 sides.
   Difference: E.g. One is regular and the other is irregular.
   / One has 5 obtuse interior angles and the other has
   right angles, acute angles and a reflex angle. / They have
   different numbers of lines of symmetry.

5) Octagon

6) No. E.g. a regular quadrilateral has 4 right angles, so
   none of the angles could be 108°. / If all four angles
   were the same they would add up to 432° not 360°.
   Yes. E.g. If the missing side was drawn parallel to the
   middle side shown, it would form a trapezium.

Page 3 — Circles

1) FALSE
   FALSE
   TRUE

2) 7 cm

3) No. E.g. The circles have diameters of 4 cm, 6 cm,
   8 cm and 10 cm. A snowman made with the three
   smallest circles will be 4 + 6 + 8 = 18 cm tall, so
   he cannot make a snowman that is 12 cm tall.

Pages 4 and 5 — 3D Shapes

1)
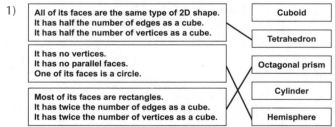

2) E.g. Top view (plan)   Side view (elevation)

3) E.g.
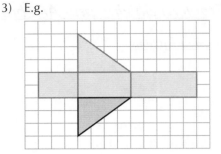

E.g.

4) Front elevation   Side elevation
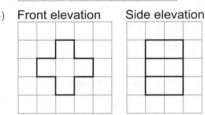

14 faces

5) E.g.

6) E.g.
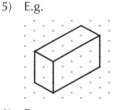

Geometry, Measures & Statistics

Pages 6 and 7 — Angles

1)

Acute	C, D
Right angle	E
Obtuse	B, G
Reflex	A, F

2)

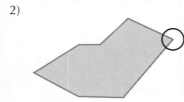

Allow 75° to 80°

3) 315°
E.g. The acute angle on the opposite side to X is about half a right angle (45°) and 360° − 45° = 315°.

4)

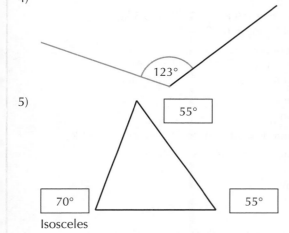

123°

5)

55°

70°   55°

Isosceles

6)

8 cm
130°   50°
6 cm
6 cm
50°   130°
X   8 cm

Pages 8 to 10 — Angle Calculations

1) $A = 30°$
($360° ÷ 12$)

2) $X = 68°$
(White triangle is isosceles, so $X = 180° − (2 × 56°)$)
$Y = 112°$
(X and Y on a straight line, so $Y = 180° − 68°$)
$Z = 68°$
($Z = X$ as they are vertically opposite)

3) No. E.g. the third angle is $180° − 37° − 106° = 37°$, so two of the angles are the same (37°). This means it cannot be scalene, as the angles would all have to be different. The triangle is isosceles.

4) 90°
($360° − 47° − 90° − 133°$)
Trapezium

5) $r = 120°$
($q = 80 ÷ 2 = 40$, $360 − 80 − 40 = 240$, $r = 240 ÷ 2$)

6) $y = 69°$, $z = 111°$
(Triangle is isosceles, so angle opposite y is 69°.
So $y = 69°$ as vertically opposite angles are equal.
Opposite angles are equal in a parallelogram,
and angles add up to 360°, so $2z = 360 − 69 − 69$,
$2z = 222$, $z = 222 ÷ 2$)

7) FALSE
TRUE
TRUE
TRUE

8) Yes. E.g. Exterior angle of a regular octagon $= 360° ÷ 8 = 45°$. The triangle is made of these two exterior angles, so the remaining angle is $180° − (2 × 45°) = 90°$, which is a right angle.

9) 1440°
(Number of sides $= 360° ÷ 36° = 10$. One interior angle $= 180° − 36° = 144°$, so sum $= 144° × 10$.)

Pages 11 and 12 — Coordinates

1) C

2)

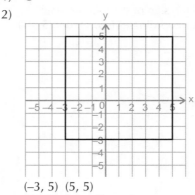

(−3, 5) (5, 5)
(5, −3) (−3, −3)

3)

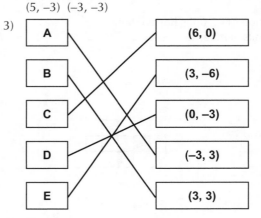

4) (7, −1)

5) (9, −2)

6) R: (−3, 0)
S: (2, −5)

Geometry, Measures & Statistics

Pages 13 and 14 — Translation and Reflection

1)

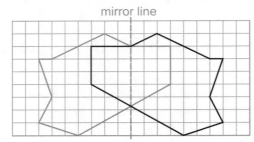
mirror line

2)

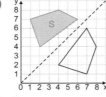

3)

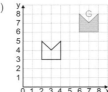

4) No
E.g. Reflecting in the x-axis will keep the x-coordinate the same, but reverse the sign of the y-coordinate.
So the image will have coordinates (−5, 1), not (5, −1).

5)

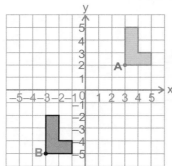

A translation of −6 units horizontally and −7 units vertically.

6) (−2, 2)
(2, −2)
(−4, 5)

7)

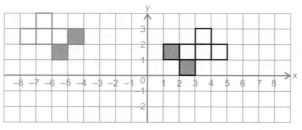

Section 2 — Measurement

Pages 15 to 19 — Units

1) 1250 ml

2) 21 740 g   1.464 cm
0.007 l   45 m

3) 0.005 km, 4.5 m, 55 cm

4) 80 ml

5) 25 mm

6) 84 cm
(30 mm = 3 cm, 4 weeks = 28 days, 3 × 28)

7)

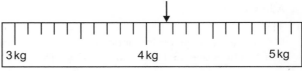

1.925 kg
(Mass of bag = 6 kg + 75 g = 6.075 kg
Mass of laptop = 6.075 − 4.15)

8) E.g. 2 pounds   64 km
10 cm   35 miles
4 pints   24 inches

9) $8\frac{1}{2}$ ounces
E.g. 680 g
($1\frac{1}{2}$ pounds = 24 ounces. 12 ounces ≈ 0.34 kg,
so 24 ounces ≈ 0.34 × 2 = 0.68 kg)

10) 4.6 l
1100 ml

11) 80 km
13.5 l
(She uses 4.5 l (1 gallon) to travel 80 km, so
she uses 4.5 × 3 gallons to travel 240 km)

12) 83 cm
(2 inches ≈ 5 cm, 22 inches ≈ 11 × 5 = 55 cm.
Total length ≈ 55 cm + 28 cm)

13) 21 miles
(Total distance = 30 + 8.5 + 1.5 = 40 km,
8 km ≈ 5 miles, 40 km ≈ 5 × 5 = 25 miles, 25 − 4)

Geometry, Measures & Statistics

Pages 20 to 22 — Time

1)

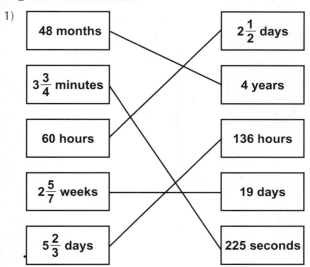

2) 3 hours and 30 minutes
($3 \times 7 \times 10 = 210$ minutes)

3) 172 800 seconds
($60 \times 60 \times 24 \times 2$)

4) 11 years and 7 months
(34 months = 2 years 10 months,
$8\frac{3}{4}$ years = 8 years 9 months.
So, in total she is 10 years and 19 months
= 10 years + 1 year + 7 months)

5) 5 hours and 25 minutes
65 minutes

6)

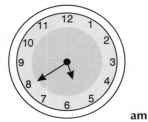

am

7) 20:54

8)

Canlaster	07:47	08:16	08:49	09:31
Vulerston	08:23	08:46	09:25	10:03
Grizesea	08:34	08:54	09:32	10:11
Eccleston	08:51	09:10	09:53	10:24
Brough Rigg	08:53	09:12	09:56	10:26
Millenden	09:09	09:25	10:11	10:40

10 minutes
08:23

Page 23 — Money

1) £1.35
Three £2 coins, a £1 coin and a 10p coin

2) £19.45
£3.25
(£39 ÷ 12)

Pages 24 to 28 — Perimeter and Area

1) 22 cm

2) A, C, D

3) 54 cm²

4) 290 m

5) 1300 cm²
($50 \times 30 = 1500$ cm², $20 \times 10 = 200$ cm², 1500 − 200)
104 cm
($1300 \times 4 = 5200$ cm². 5200 ÷ 50)
40 cm
200 cm

6) 18 m

7) E.g.

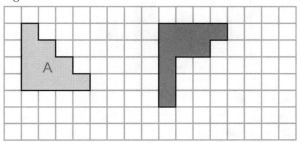

8) 30 cm²
(a 6 cm × 5 cm rectangle also has a perimeter of 22 cm)

9) 84 m²
($\frac{1}{2} \times 14 \times 12$)

10) 270 cm²

11) 12 cm²
($\frac{1}{2} \times 4 \times 5 = 10$ cm², $1 \times 2 = 2$ cm², 10 + 2)
40 cm²

12) 92 cm²
(area of flag = $10 \times 12 = 120$ cm²,
base of parallelogram = 12 − 5 = 7 cm
area of parallelogram = $7 \times 4 = 28$ cm²
so shaded area = 120 − 28)

13) 5
(area of 6 rectangles + 4 triangles = 220 cm²
each rectangle is $3 \times 10 = 30$ cm²,
so 6 rectangles = $6 \times 30 = 180$ cm²
so 4 triangles = 220 − 180 = 40 cm²
so 1 triangle = 40 ÷ 4 = 10 cm²
each triangle is $\frac{1}{2} \times 4 \times y = 2y = 10$ cm², so $y = 10 \div 2$)

Pages 29 and 30 — Volume

1) 108 cm³

2) 4

3) 2
(The tower has $5 \times 4 = 20$ rooms, so each
room has a volume of 600 ÷ 20 = 30 m³,
room volume = $5 \times 3 \times p = 15p$ m³, $p = 30 \div 15$)

4) 100 cm³
20 slices

5) 0.6 m³
(Volume of hole = $0.5 \times 1.6 \times 0.5 = 0.4$ m³
Volume of wood = $(2 \times 0.5 \times 1.4) - (2 \times 0.4)$
= 1.4 − 0.8)

Geometry, Measures & Statistics

Section 3 — Statistics

Pages 31 to 36 — Tables, Charts and Graphs

1) The row in the table for Misha looks like this:

Misha	2	0	5	6	7

2)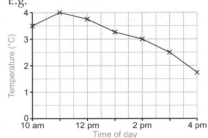

24 songs
60 songs

3) 0.3 km
135 minutes

4) E.g.

5) Yes. E.g. in month 1, the pond was 150 cm deep and in month 4, the pond was 50 cm deep.
150 ÷ 3 = 50, so the pond was one third as deep in month 4.

6) 40 mph
13 seconds

7) $5
£40

8) Chocolate
False. E.g. the actual number of adults and children that said pizza are unknown. The chart only shows that a smaller proportion of children said pizza.

9) $\frac{1}{4}$

Japan: 45
Greece: 60
Australia: 30

10) 60
35
(E.g. 360 ÷ 60 = 6, so each player is represented by 6°.
30 ÷ 6 = 5, so there are five 10-year-olds.
60 − 15 − 5 = 40, so there are forty 12-year-olds.
So there are 40 − 5 = 35 more 12-year-olds than 10-year-olds.)

11)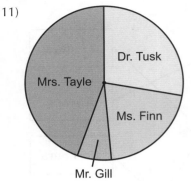

Dr. Tusk: 100°
Ms. Finn: 75°
Mr. Gill: 25°
Mrs. Tayle: 160°

$\frac{5}{9}$

Pages 37 to 39 — Analysing Data

1) 37 cm
(35 + 32 + 48 + 45 + 25 = 185, 185 ÷ 5)

2) Ribble Rovers
(Umbridge United has 8 × 4 = 32 wins.
Ribble Rovers has 9 + 8 + 6 + 14 = 37 wins.)

3) 50
(880 + 450 + 850 + 220 = 2400, 2400 ÷ 4 = 600.
1050 + 150 + 400 + 1000 + 450 + 250 = 3300,
3300 ÷ 6 = 550. So difference is 600 − 550)
350

4) 5 °C

5) £1.55

6) 8, 11, 14

7) £30 000
£1800
(£2000 × 10 = £20 000, £200 × 5 = £1000.
£20 000 + £1000 = £21 000.
£30 000 − £21 000 = £9000.
£9000 ÷ 5)

Arithmetic

Arithmetic
Section 1
— Whole Numbers

Pages 1 and 2 — Written Addition

1) 5397
2) 6889
3) 2542
4) 8893
5) 28 184
6) 19 899
7) 75 985
8) 60 938
9) 55 629
10) 91 732
11) 106 624
12) 115 645
13) 59 071
14) 90 377
15) 28 708
16) 49 625
17) 842 016
18) 2 202 328

Pages 3 and 4
— Written Subtraction

1) 3934
2) 5313
3) 1867
4) 1781
5) 2233
6) 32 401
7) 70 071
8) 52 050
9) 22 038
10) 40 665
11) 121
12) 23 003
13) 39 412
14) 92 188
15) 12 493
16) 433 519
17) 367 171
18) 7 875 317

Page 5 — Multiplying
by 10, 100 and 1000

1) 23 400
2) 67 350
3) 610 000
4) 9 896 000
5) 7 050 000
6) 110 100
7) 2 222 000
8) 89 000 000

Page 6 — Dividing
by 10, 100 and 1000

1) 8
2) 21
3) 860
4) 99
5) 805
6) 1690
7) 9090
8) 6210

Page 7 — Using Times Tables

1) 15 000
2) 84 000
3) 72 000
4) 121 000
5) 400
6) 5
7) 90
8) 80

Page 8 — Multiples and Factors

1) 120, 240, 360, 480, 600, 720
2) 75, 150, 225, 300, 375, 450
3) 42, 84, 126, 168, 210, 252
4) 36, 72
5) 1, 2, 7, 14, 49, 98
6) 1, 3, 5, 7, 15, 21, 35, 105
7) 1, 3, 9

Pages 9 and 10 —
Short Multiplication

1) 642
2) 6251
3) 3132
4) 1736
5) 24 318
6) 49 380
7) 23 784
8) 42 776
9) 53 823
10) 61 641
11) 18 872
12) 53 790
13) 88 884
14) 60 656

Arithmetic

Pages 11 and 12 — Long Multiplication

1) 9264

2) 25 671
Working: 597
          ×   43
          _____
           1791
          23880
          _____
          25671

3) 35 840
Working: 1024
          ×   35
          _____
           5120
          30720
          _____
          35840

4) 150 276
Working: 3578
          ×   42
          _____
           7156
          143120
          _____
          150276

5) 377 188
Working: 4963
          ×   76
          _____
          29778
          347410
          _____
          377188

6) 405 168
Working: 5872
          ×   69
          _____
          52848
          352320
          _____
          405168

7) 571 002
Working: 9678
          ×   59
          _____
          87102
          483900
          _____
          571002

8) 446 338
Working: 9703
          ×   46
          _____
          58218
          388120
          _____
          446338

9) 674 856
Working: 8652
          ×   78
          _____
          69216
          605640
          _____
          674856

10) 749 602
Working: 7649
          ×   98
          _____
          61192
          688410
          _____
          749602

Page 13 — Short Division with No Remainders

1) 125
2) 94
3) 1269
4) 934
5) 857
6) 145
7) 416
8) 583

Pages 14 and 15 — Short Division with Remainders

1) 248 r 2
2) 134 r 4
3) 1398 r 2
4) 786 r 6
5) 238 r 3
6) 341 r 10
7) 154 r 8
8) 673 r 6
9) $158\frac{3}{4}$
10) $187\frac{2}{5}$
11) $192\frac{1}{4}$
12) $252\frac{4}{7}$
13) $391\frac{1}{12}$
14) $142\frac{1}{8}$
15) $279\frac{4}{5}$
16) $265\frac{3}{7}$

Pages 16 and 17 — Long Division with No Remainders

1) 32

2) 54
Working:
        5 4
    17) 9 1 8
        − 8 5
        _____
          6 8
        − 6 8
        _____
            0

3) 41
Working:
          4 1
    39) 1 5 9 9
        − 1 5 6
        _____
            3 9
          − 3 9
        _____
              0

4) 23
Working:
          2 3
    44) 1 0 1 2
        − 8 8
        _____
           1 3 2
         − 1 3 2
        _____
              0

5) 345

Working:

```
        3 4 5
  19 ⌐6 5 5 5
    - 5 7
        8 5
      - 7 6
          9 5
        - 9 5
            0
```

6) 218

Working:

```
        2 1 8
  27 ⌐5 8 8 6
    - 5 4
        4 8
      - 2 7
          2 1 6
        - 2 1 6
              0
```

7) 76

Working:

```
          7 6
  34 ⌐2 5 8 4
    - 2 3 8
        2 0 4
      - 2 0 4
            0
```

8) 89

Working:

```
          8 9
  67 ⌐5 9 6 3
    - 5 3 6
        6 0 3
      - 6 0 3
            0
```

Page 18 — Long Division with Remainders

1) 279 r 4

Working:

```
        2 7 9
  15 ⌐4 1 8 9
    - 3 0
        1 1 8
      - 1 0 5
          1 3 9
        - 1 3 5
              4
```

2) 287 r 10

Working:

```
        2 8 7
  32 ⌐9 1 9 4
    - 6 4
        2 7 9
      - 2 5 6
          2 3 4
        - 2 2 4
            1 0
```

3) $309\frac{1}{7}$

Working:

```
        3 0 9
  28 ⌐8 6 5 6
    - 8 4
        2 5
      - 0
        2 5 6
      - 2 5 2
            4
```

4) $167\frac{1}{4}$

Working:

```
        1 6 7
  52 ⌐8 6 9 7
    - 5 2
        3 4 9
      - 3 1 2
          3 7 7
        - 3 6 4
            1 3
```

Page 19 — Mixed Questions

1) 86
2) 85
3) 22
4) 88
5) 1
6) 35

Section 2 — Decimals

Page 20 — Adding Decimals

1) 54.91
2) 12.42
3) 9.842
4) 6.098
5) 4.189
6) 25.617
7) 111.001
8) 200.646

Page 21 — Subtracting Decimals

1) 5.25
2) 11.68
3) 0.982
4) 3.589
5) 6.013
6) 4.875
7) 3.725
8) 16.621

Page 22 — Multiplying by 10, 100 and 1000

1) 91.3
2) 5549.8
3) 980
4) 8708.7
5) 1 121 130
6) 450
7) 39 030
8) 12 022

Page 23 — Dividing by 10, 100 and 1000

1) 812.5
2) 883.4
3) 0.107
4) 90.022
5) 308.512
6) 710.3
7) 1.03
8) 80.1

Arithmetic

Pages 24 and 25 — Multiplying with Decimals

1) 73.8
2) 53.6
3) 92.4
4) 1.68
5) 4.35
6) 36.72
7) 63.21
8) 28.96
9) 96.15
10) 280.84
11) 175.52
12) 535.14
13) 623.72
14) 3897.71

Pages 26 and 27 — Short and Long Division with Decimals

1) 173.2
2) 114.75
3) 97.25
4) 249.6
5) 2228.5
6) 631.5
7) 2493.75
8) 1853.5

9) 233.5
Working:
```
        2 3 3 . 5
  24 ) 5 6 0 4 . 0
      - 4 8
        8 0
      - 7 2
        8 4
      - 7 2
        1 2 0
      - 1 2 0
            0
```

10) 236.75
Working:
```
        2 3 6 . 7 5
  16 ) 3 7 8 8 . 0 0
      - 3 2
        5 8
      - 4 8
        1 0 8
      -  9 6
        1 2 0
      - 1 1 2
            8 0
          - 8 0
              0
```

11) 202.75
Working:
```
        2 0 2 . 7 5
  36 ) 7 2 9 9 . 0 0
      - 7 2
        0 9
      -  0
        9 9
      - 7 2
        2 7 0
      - 2 5 2
          1 8 0
        - 1 8 0
              0
```

12) 312.8
Working:
```
        3 1 2 . 8
  35 ) 1 0 9 4 8 . 0
      - 1 0 5
          4 4
        - 3 5
          9 8
        - 7 0
          2 8 0
        - 2 8 0
              0
```

Pages 28 and 29 — Adding Fractions

1) $\frac{11}{15}$
2) $\frac{11}{14}$
3) $\frac{19}{20}$
4) $\frac{3}{4}$
5) $\frac{37}{32}$
6) $\frac{19}{20}$
7) $\frac{7}{3}$
8) $\frac{9}{5}$
9) $\frac{19}{15}$
10) $\frac{38}{55}$
11) $\frac{13}{24}$
12) $\frac{37}{30}$
13) $\frac{73}{60}$
14) $\frac{65}{48}$
15) $\frac{7}{6}$
16) $\frac{49}{60}$

Arithmetic

Pages 30 and 31 — Subtracting Fractions

1) $\frac{5}{16}$
2) $\frac{1}{6}$
3) $\frac{11}{16}$
4) $\frac{3}{8}$
5) $-\frac{7}{16}$
6) $\frac{29}{24}$
7) $\frac{107}{25}$
8) $\frac{1}{12}$
9) $\frac{7}{20}$
10) $\frac{17}{88}$
11) $\frac{8}{15}$
12) $\frac{7}{24}$
13) $\frac{37}{36}$
14) $\frac{47}{50}$
15) $\frac{4}{15}$
16) $\frac{17}{60}$

Pages 32 and 33 — Mixed Numbers

1) $5\frac{3}{4}$
2) $3\frac{13}{16}$
3) $7\frac{1}{2}$
4) $3\frac{7}{18}$
5) $5\frac{1}{6}$
6) $6\frac{5}{12}$
7) $3\frac{7}{15}$
8) $2\frac{19}{30}$
9) $7\frac{17}{24}$
10) $1\frac{13}{20}$
11) $3\frac{23}{36}$
12) $6\frac{7}{12}$

Pages 34 and 35 — Multiplying Fractions

1) $\frac{4}{7}$
2) $\frac{1}{12}$
3) $\frac{10}{27}$
4) $\frac{9}{55}$
5) $\frac{5}{8}$
6) $\frac{1}{40}$
7) $\frac{11}{39}$
8) $\frac{17}{125}$
9) $7\frac{3}{7}$
10) $24\frac{8}{15}$
11) $20\frac{4}{5}$
12) $51\frac{3}{7}$
13) 26
14) 81
15) 94
16) 1125

Page 36 — Dividing Fractions

1) $\frac{1}{20}$
2) $\frac{1}{40}$
3) $\frac{2}{21}$
4) $\frac{4}{81}$
5) $\frac{5}{39}$
6) $\frac{11}{100}$
7) $\frac{1}{24}$
8) $\frac{3}{14}$

Pages 37 and 38 — Percentages

1) 48
2) 72
3) 170
4) 126
5) 4.4
6) 112
7) 6.6
8) 20.4
9) 36
10) 96
11) 17
12) 594
13) 6.6
14) 248
15) 31.5
16) 360

Page 39 — Decimals, Fractions and Percentages

1) 18%
2) 0.125
3) 8.5%
4) $\frac{6}{25}$
5) $\frac{11}{20}$
6) 0.875

ISBN 978 1 78294 859 9

9 781782 948599

M6HA21

£2.00
(Retail Price)

ORNITHOLO

Photography *by* Andrew Fusek

Poems *by* Philip Rush

ORNITHOLOGY

By and large the **poems** and *photographs* have been ordered
following the taxonomy in Collins.

GEOFFREY CHAUCER
HIS GUIDE TO ENGLISH BIRDS
from 'The Parliament of Fowls'

That is to seyn, the foules of ravyne
Weere hyest set; and thans the foules smale,
That eten as hem Nature wolde enclyne,
As worm or thyng of which I telle no tale;
And water-foul sat lowest in the dale;
But foul that lyveth by sed sat on the grene,
And that so fele, that wonder was to sene.

There myghte men the royal egle fynde,
That with his sharpe lok perseth the sonne,
And othere egles of a lowere kynde,
Of which that clerkes wel devysen conne.
Ther was the tiraunt with his fetheres donne
And grey, I mene the goshauk, that doth pyne
To bryddes for his outrageous ravyne.

The gentyl faucoun, that with his feet distrayneth
The kynges hond; the hardy sperhauk eke,
The quayles foo; the merlioun that payneth
Hymself ful ofte, the larke for to seke;
There was the douve, with hire yën meke;
The jelous swan, ayens his deth that syngeth;
The oule ek, that of deth the bode bryngeth;

The crane the geaunt, with his trompes soun;
The thef, the chough; and ek the janglynge pye;
The skornynge jay; the eles foo, heroun;
The false lapwynge, ful of trecherye;
The stare, that the counseyl can bewrye;
The tame ruddok; and the coward kyte;
The cok, that orloge is of thorpes lyte;

The sparwe, Venus sone; the nyghtyngale,
That clepeth forth the grene leves newe;
The swalwe, mortherere of the foules smale
That maken hony of floures freshe of hewe;
The wedded turtil, with hire herte trewe;
The pekok, with his aungels fetheres bryghte;
The fesaunt, skornere of the cok by nyghte;

The waker goos; the cukkow ever unkynde;
The popynjay, ful of delicasye;
The drake, stroyere of his owene kynde;
The stork, the wrekere of avouterye;
The hote cormeraunt of glotenye;
The raven wys; the crow with vois of care;
The throstil olde; the frosty feldefare.

APRIL & EVENING

Nothing seems to make the slightest sense.
 This morning the sky again, harriers,
pipits, and everything in the present tense.

We stop above Broughton to help a cyclist
 and there are buzzards along the Duddon
though nothing seems to make the slightest sense.

What a graceful bird the merganser is,
 his preening, his oiling, his Teddy Boy quiff,
his classy comfort with the present tense.

It's more than a trait, my dad's forgetfulness -
 he's disorientated and edgy
and nothing seems to make the slightest sense.

He's as lost as a passage migrant, yes,
 a winter visitor. He needs Mum nearby.
For him, everything's in the present tense.

April and evening put cold gloves against
 our cheeks. Two swans settle down for the night.
But nothing seems to make the slightest sense.
 Everything exists in the present tense.

RAPTURE

The bird-hide is a chapel.
Its peculiar rules & its pecking order.
Its silence, its pews and its disapprovals.
And I swear I saw the binoculars gang
bless themselves at the door.

The chapel is a bird-hide.
The grim faithful.
Their fidgeting with apparatus.
The eccentric hours they keep.
And the long, dim vigils, waiting

for the great egret to announce
itself. Or the black-tailed godwit.
The eager haloes of the reeds,
their tongues of fire, backlit,
combed and troubled by the wind.

HERON

The heron
stands still,
the perfect
calligraphy
of heron.

Which
combines
the hunt
and the monk
at meditation.

Heron.

It may be
Vergil,
it may be
Dante,
or I think
this time

quite
possibly

it might be
Norman
Nicholson
with his
whiskers
and his
Blue
Peter
badges.

BUTTERFLIES &
VULTURES

My dad died in Boltaña
far from the sea.
The martins brought the news
as they brought so many things
but chiefly flies
to their nests tucked
into these tall eaves.

The day my dad died
we'd been in the mountains
with butterflies & vultures.
Butterflies and vultures
from deep dark places
full of chrysalids
and thermals.

Which rise
actual and invisible
amongst rocks
and cliffs and gorges.
Which funnel
the sound of water
out into thin air.

My dad died
in Boltaña
far from the sea.
The martins
brought the news
as they bring
so many things.

DEAR ANDREW

There's authority
in your photo
of the red kite,
its colours sharp
as a bradawl and full
of savoury words
such as chestnut, umber,
ochre and russet.
The winter end
of autumn, last year's
growth a paler shade
of brown amongst
the black-as-Newgate's-
knocker black.
St Lawrence was hazy
when we saw her
with her stilly wing
and forked tail
on border patrol
beside the flood
and the Milebrook.
But a camera cannot
catch the kiteness
of the kite, the muscular
wrench and wrestle
with the wind,
the twist and flex.
An invisible line
binds kite to earth
without which
she could not somersault
and dovetail and pike
in the rainbow air.
This time of year
the hillsides are cloyed
by rainfall. Which
seeps and whispers
into the valley streams.

ICONS

Glossy ploughland
north-east of Walsingham
is well-versed in the Bible.

The flint-work cottages
are rich with statues
of the Virgin Mary.

Over Langham aerodrome
a buzzard lumbers up
into the sky,

wings spread-eagled,
tail trimmed, flaps down,
and huge yellow talons tucked up tight.

SPARROWHAWK

You may be familiar with the 'Mach-loop',
the marriage between the speed of sound
and the glaciated valleys around
the Centre for Alternative Technology.

In which case you'll know what I mean
when I describe the sparrowhawk at Cors Caron,
who, having helped himself from the feeding station,
sped with prey in his claws away towards the trees.

And, on seeing us, spun on a sixpence, activated
his swing-wing avionics, splayed his tail
and afterburned through the hazel,
the young willows, and the late sun,

to leave nothing but a sudden huge roar
and a fluttering amongst the thin hedgerow.

CAUGHT THIS MORNING

How beautiful the slope is!
It has never seemed so beautiful before
with its ripening grain and new-mown hay.
Brennu-Njáls Saga

Some floozy in a fancy dress has Photoshopped
the woods, the usual woods, and they have such deep reds
this early October morning it's stopped us dead
in our tracks. I'm texting friends when the penny drops

and suddenly I know who I am. I'm Gunnar,
riding down to the rough strand at Hliðarendi
when his horse stumbles, he falls to the turf and he
looks back up to the angel landscape he adores.

I do not want to leave. This huge crimson dawn
someone's crayoned, this colour-me-in of Standish,
maybe young Lawrence, whose work is better finished
now his specs work. But I can't stand here all morning.

Even though there's a kestrel engaging the fierce wind,
living origami, a page ripped from something.

ESCAPE VELOCITY

Fifty minutes along the towpath.
A reach of rectangular water
slopping and dull. Four sulking
gulls and a man in huge boots.
A small, damp breeze.

A herd of black, Gainsborough cows.
A small flock of maybe eight
tubby sheep. And, through winter trees,
the conning towers of the Slimbridge
submarine, its wildfowl braying like a kennels.

And what should appear gunning down
the waterway but a peregrine falcon
in Fleet Air Arm livery, tucking its wings
to its sides and bulleting the dusk.
Tiny, feathered, shark.

PURPLE SANDPIPERS

Down by the shore yesterday
two small birds were feeding.
They jabbed their long beaks
into the kelps and the stuff
that had been washed ashore.
Maybe for flies or small crabs.

A pair, they were never more
than a foot or so apart.
When the sea washed towards them,
the tide flowing and the wind
strengthening, they gave together
a little skip on tiny legs.

We laughed to see ourselves.
Above, huge buzzards
sauntered across the sky –
beyond, cormorants
in black suits and glossy
dived into the dark waters.

JANET'S
FOSS

It's a gobstopper
of a rock,
a streaked
humbug.
The music of water
under its breath
hums along
with curlews.
Wagtails do
their tufa dance.
The air is
different here.
It breathes
more heavily.
It is weighted
with age.
The ramsons
burn
their joss-stick
green.

The music
of the curlew
harmonizes
the force
of water.
Sometimes
we are taken
where we
do not want
to go.
Sometimes
we chance
on something
we might call
beauty.
A humble beck
is anointed
by the falls.
It is a small
wonder.

the first days of Spring
and beck-water hums along
to the curlews' tune

TERN

Coquettish
as a First Communion dress
she dances her soft Spitfire,

drops like broken scissors
into the formal water
to snap small fry

which she swallows on the wing.
She's an attacking full-back
crammed with craft.

Yes, your tern has Tom-Tommed
from South Africa,
hardwired for the long haul.

SPURS' PROGRESS

I know exactly how much a barn owl is worth,
because a weird thing happened to me yesterday.
It's midnight. I am driving home on the M40
from the Spurs-Milan game
which was a 0-0 win to Tottenham —
by the way, I have gone for the present tense
to give the story zap and a sense of absolute truth —

I am driving home on the M40 and there is a new moon.
We're listening to a daft phone-in on Radio 5
where they are asking people
about situations where they've
"carried on regardless"
and we're making fun of this
with our superior wit and know-how.

We've gone down the edge of the Chilterns,
the Vicar of Dibley bit,
and I remember saying to Aidan,
It feels like they've stretched the motorway,
I've usually turned off for Oxford by now,
and then we pass a sign for the services,
seventeen miles ahead.

And I'm like, This is getting a bit strange,
but I carry on regardless
and after maybe twenty minutes
what should loom up out of the drizzly, nasty night
but a sign for the A43 and Silverstone.
My mortification is complete. I am a fool
and miles off course. I almost want to screech out loud.

So we're off at Middleton Stony
and I find the Witney road,
dredged up from some old memory,
and we wriggle across north Oxfordshire,
carefully looking left and right at every junction,
through villages with names which sound all wrong
and no traffic apart from police cars.

Until, near Long Hanborough,
or somewhere,
there's a barn owl on a post,
preening itself and full of poetry,
well, metaphor.
It's half dalek and half soft furnishings,
for a start, and it has a face like a carnivorous plant.

And where the barn owl ends and the pole begins
recalls a wood-carver's *trompe-l'oeil*.
We slow down and stare,
just for a moment,
and our hearts in hiding, etc,
and the whole crazy diversion
seems suddenly worthwhile.

That
and the fact that as the headlights
swooped tentatively round the field bends
we caught glimpses of the soil of central England,
the glossy brown corduroy of central England.
Such super tilth, I said to Aidan.
Top tilth, he replied.

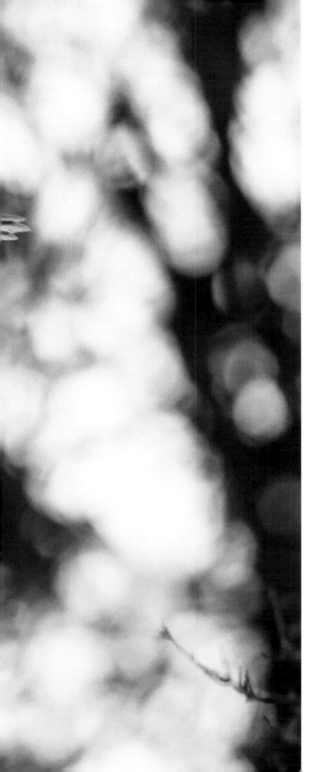

It's half dalek and half soft furnishings,
for a start,
and it has a face like a carnivorous plant.

FISHERMARTIN

The kingfisher's
        crucifixion
                is its
open arms.
        Its vestments
                are iridescent.
They absorb
        what light there is
                to filter
& radiate.
        Above the deep cello
of slow water
        kingfisher is colour
at the speed of flight.
        Heart-leaper,
                eye-catcher,
a stirrer of spirits.
        You can love it
for what it is,
        music to the eye.
You can love it
        for what it means,
                that nature
has somehow
        despite all this greed
                all this
urgency for tomorrow
        survived
in fragments
        here & there
                unblemished.
You can love it best
        because love
                is what
we do.
        And fragments
                is what we are.

SUCH LARKS

On the causeway
    across the 'tierra de campos'
        between the Town of One Hundred Virgins
            and the Little Pavement by a River
there was one hell of a row between two of the pilgrims.

Tom — an American —
    had taken boxing lessons
        back in St Louis
            to improve his musculature he said
    but also for the hell of it
        according to Ezra
            who in his day
                had boxed in Paris against Hemingway.

Tom took up his stance
    like he was a Rodin model
        or more precisely
    like he was trying to pull a broad
        by aping a Rodin model —
            and called Geoff out
                for opinions regarding April and cruelty.

Right there and right then
    April was at its cruellest
        spitting cold rain in the faces of the pilgrims
            who were gravelling along the causeway
        drenching the elaborate
            state-of-the-art wetwear
                that made them siblings of the great outdoors —
    and generally mucking everything up.

We all knew that.

But Geoffrey cocked his ear
            and in an elaborate tone
                        exquisite diction
                                    and an accent which paid
                                                remarkable attention to the final syllables of words
                        in a way you still hear if in pubs and markets
                                    and all-night coin-op laundrettes
                                                you attend to the people of Derbyshire
            Geoff cocked his ear
                        and said listen
                                    (basically)

and we listened
            and we could hear larks
                        many larks
                                    larks with a whole range
                                                of exquisite binomials

and corn buntings
            who have their own take
                        on scansion
                                    metre
                                    the iambic pentameter
                                    rime royal
                                    and middle-English prosody in general

                        with their own version of a little bread and no cheese
                                    (all the birds of Oxfordshire and Gloucestershire)

and then
        the *pièce de résistance*
                a cuckoo
                        clear as day
                a cuckoo
                        giving it large from a small stand of poplars
and as we listened
        to larks and buntings
        and a burst of goldfinches
                dressed as toy bikers and gunning the incline out of Chalford
        and the mighty cuckoo —
and as Tom held his pose
        like the prick he is

Geoffrey
        who as a customs officer
                has to deal with the awkward customer
                        more often than now and again
        stepped through Tom's defence
                like Tom's defence was a kissing gate near Minchinhampton
        and laid him out
                right there
                        on the cold, cold ground.

Free verse, scoffed Geoffrey
        as he picked up his walking stick and walked.

                Let your free verse get you up out of that one,
                    mon semblable,
                        mon frère.

CRAG MARTINS

Are fistfuls of wet sand
    flung into the sky.
Their natural instability
    keeps them on the edge.
A jogger holds his balance
    down the rocky
and uneven paths
    by dancing a fluent
& repeated stumble.
    In his headphones
is the sound of crag martins,
    their flute ostinati,
the bass rumble of the swell,
    the surf's ride cymbals.
Not even the jogger can imagine
    not even the biker
on the N-634
    what it is to be at the controls
of a cliff-top crag martin,
    the manoeuvres & gymnastics
and the scrap of a tune
    lodged in his mind
playing over
    and over again
whose meaning is deferred
    by fragmentation
and by apparently endless repetition.
    It's unlikely, I guess,
that the martins are stuck
    with the hook
from Blondie's *One Way or Another*
    or the riff

from *Heart of the Sunrise*
    but you get the picture.
The waves below which break
    against the rocks.
The rocks which break
    against the waves,
the deep ocean,
    the long
and abstract
    and unplayable sky.

ORNITHOLOGY

At the margins between forest
and moorland, there's the distinctive
and invisible call-sign cough
of capercaillie — champagne corks.

A family of peregrine
falcons fuss, fidget and squabble
in Lezama's tall church tower.
They are late night party pilgrims.

Cetti's warbler is a bullrush
gymnast, hiccupping noisily.

SWALLOW BALLAD
28th July 2010

The swifts and martins
are demonstrating Brownian motion
in the blue, blue volume
of their sky.

You can judge their position
or estimate their speed,
but never both. They strive
to break the light barrier.

Above them, a vulture soars.
Above the vulture, one at a time,
huge silver-white aeroplanes
and their incredible physics.

SWALLOW BALLAD
after Eduardo Fraile Valles

The swallows bring me
        the dark night
of their wings. They cut
        their disc of light
into perfect fractions,
        each time more tightly,
each time more hurriedly,
        as they reach their full height,
their zenith, where I can
        no longer follow their flight
because it is so much faster,
        so much faster than sight.

PICA PICA URRACA

Someone has left the door open
and the Arctic is simpering in
with the smell of a damp dog
and a hint of that feeling you get
in your fingers after snow.

The car is crystalled with ice
the fields are frosted
like Corn Flakes can be frosted
and the temperature inversion
in the valley will get the cameras out.

On every perch round here
is a magpie talking magpie
in a loud voice with no respect
for the neighbours and no sense
of propriety. Magpies.

Half crow half gull all
bark and all fishwife.
The fieldfares I can take
though they only show up
for the fruit picking.

The blackcaps I love
the way you can rely on them
to pull in twice a year
to the lay-by for a night or two
tea brewing on the open fire.

And the buzzards
have settled amongst
the tall trees beside the lake.
But magpies. They have shamed
their own magic.

They are dancers
from the *Folies Bergère*
so many of them
shopping at Tesco naked
but for a golden chain.

GOLDCREST ONLY DANCING

Goldcrest's engineering places him
      close to the Alfa-Romeo end
of the market. Goldcrest
      does a real neat turn.

Goldcrest green is a brushstroke green,
      a glamrock green, a sugary pastry green.
Goldcrest stares me out –
      first one and then the other eye.

For no more than
      the weak heartbeat of a tiny bird
I see the whole complicated
      world through a goldcrest lens.

He is dancing and trapezing.
      His bright smear of egg yolk & sunlight
bobs amongst the twigs.
      He's a playground child.

Goldcrest would sing a bar or two
      of his favourite song,
the first song we grow deaf to as we age.
      But he has to be off.

LIFE DRAWING

A pencil helps the eyes,
a stick of charcoal,
the way a hand-held digital recorder
helps the ears.

Miles from home
and an earthy wind,
the sunflower fields
an open-air market for rag-dolls.

Or dawn rain
in a forlorn, mountainous landscape,
how it requires an imaginative use
of the materials at hand.

Or drizzle
singing in a strange language,
the woodpecker's
flight a hiccough.

Words gather and twinkle
like long-tailed tits in a Norfolk winter,
like a headline
whose connotations are lost to you.

EVEN RAVENS, EVEN RAVENS'
HAVE NEVER SEEN THE WIND

Julian proposes a toast to Yoko.
Of course, I can't hear him at first. The gale —
all fifty-five-miles-an-hour of it — blows
his voice away, turns it into a gull

and tosses it aside. Typical Skye.
The bay of Duntulm is far below.
Spume, spray and the road sags as a bus goes by.
From the abandoned hotel, ravens throw

themselves into the storm. They are demons.
They draw roller-coasters in the cold air.
They croak rustily above the headland.
They wall-of-death the wind, swoop and swagger.

URBAN ORNITHOLOGY

'It's Goldfinch Time!'
scream the goldfinches
as they run amok

in their team colours
all over town.
'I'm starving,' say the ravens.

'A little bit of bread
and no cheese,'
says the yellow-hammer

at the cathedral door.

THE EARTH
SINGS A NEW SONG

As hard as I look, as
closely as I examine
this square yard of

squabbling landscape, this
spring, this fountainhead, this
new-born water, purified and filtered,

I cannot see the sound I can hear,
the sound
of cold water boiling.

The whole tiny view
is packed
with corny haiku.

There are sunlit bluebells
and anemones in the clean air,
little green fronds paddling.

This tiny water plays
a pedal point
for all that lucid, angry bird song.

The rooks are doing that thing
with their beaks that storks do.
Our stream strengthens on new legs,

cleansing as baptism
in a text by Aquinas or Anselm
preserved

in some dusty hermitage or other.

CROWSKY

Crows love onomatopoeia.
They're all over onomatopoeia.
They are big, juicy crayons
on grey misty paper the colour of sky.
They write their names all over the woods.

The brambles reach out their bony fingers,
salivate maliciously.
Things seem different now.
Van Gogh's been up for a start,
and he's given the place a makeover.

Extra crows have been imported
and they've been rehearsing
a whole new song and dance sequence.
There is the special light of thunder.
The corn has been harvested

and everyone remembers the noise,
like they'd opened a sugar beet
factory in the old quarry,
or were resurfacing the fields.
Which in a way they were.

The whole hillside has been laid
waste into a cross between
the final landscape and Chapter One
of The Approach to Latin —
vasto vastare vastavi vastatum.

BACKSTAGE
AT THE
MURMURATIONS

Where the wild moorland
meets the narrow road
gather the starlings
massing
for the evening raid
on Aberystwyth
in a flash-mob of skitter.

Not such wild moorland,
to be honest,
just a lot of it.
No wolves, no dragons
bar those to be drawn
lifesize and wonderful
in the sky.

HAPPY

Every goldfinch has a haiku
drawn in brushwork
on the lower surface
of its wings.

A sudden nothing spooks them all.
They disappear into the sycamore.
Their flight draws
perfect slurs in the air.

Though one day
you may find them again,
by chance or in mist-nets
which you have set deliberately,

you will be surprised
by how many years have passed,
by quite how old
you have become.

FEAST DAY

The goldfinches believe
in a benevolent god.
It is the only explanation
which makes any sense.

One has decided that a flourish
of wings from above the hazel
constitutes a prayer.
Another sits on his lucky branch

and thanks the Lord
for how beautiful he looks,
for how much more

sophisticated he is
than a siskin
or a two-a-penny sparrow.

GRAINS OF WHEAT

Today the haiku garden –
hedge sparrow, coal tit,
bullfinch, goldfinch, long-tailed tit,
woodpecker and snow.

BACKING SINGERS

I am enamoured this morning
        of two female bullfinches.
Like Doré, Giacomelli
        and Geoff Hurst's third goal
against West Germany,
        their beauty's in black and white.
Despite their shared DNA,
        they are not to be muddled with
bullfrogs or bulrushes.
        They do not flinch or retreat
when the male trundles in
        with his martyr's muleta
and his unearthly nobility.
        (As Ernest Hemingway puts it
in his short book on garden birds.)
        They introduce a minor key
to the fuss and business
        at the foot of the hazel tree.
Their deportment and their sisterhood
        are second to none.
They're acrobats in Armani.

BIRDSONG

That birdsong stakes a claim
for land and territory,
for status and sex,

comes as no surprise
to those of us who've tuned in
to human conversation.

Andrew Fusek Peters is an award winning wildlife, garden and landscape photographer based in Shropshire. His photos regularly appear in the national papers and camera magazines. He was awarded Highly Commended in British Wildlife Photographer of the Year 2018 and Commended and 3rd in Category for International Garden Photographer of the Year 2019. His supermoon made the front cover of the Times and the cover of Amateur Photographer.

Philip Rush runs Yew Tree Press in Stroud which produces pamphlets for local and not-so-local poets. A selection of his work appeared in Carcanet's *New Poetries IV* and his first book of poems, *Big Purple Garden Paintings*, was short-listed for the Aldeburgh First Collection Prize. He has won the Ledbury poetry competition and his poems can be found in issues of magazines in the UK, Ireland and the USA.

Acknowledgement is made to the publications where some of these photographs were originally to be found. The front cover robin was published in *The Times* and on the cover of *EOS* magazine; sparrowhawk taking a collared dove was in *The Times*, and *Times Picture of the Day* online; robin, skylark and cuckoo in *Photoplus Magazine*.

Some of the poems in this book have been published elsewhere, sometimes in slightly different versions. *Dear Andrew*, which is many ways is the cornerstone of the book, was published by Bloodaxe in their anthology *Hwæt!*; *Spurs' Progress* was published by Stroud Short Stories; *Sparrowhawk* was published in Obsessed with Pipework; *Butterflies and Vultures*, *Purple Sandpipers*, *Fishermartin*, *Ornithology*, *Two Swallow Ballads*, *Goldcrest Only Dancing*, *Even Ravens*, *Happy* and *Birdsong* were in limited edition pamphlets from Yew Tree Press.